Contents

Introduction

Collins Mental Maths is a series designed to help children develop effective strategies to carry out mental calculations and acquire a 'feel' for number.

The series is built around three beliefs:

- Being good at mental mathematics raises children's mathematical achievement considerably;

- Teachers can play a very important part in training children, by offering focused lessons, to develop the most efficient strategies for mental maths and acquire sound technical fluency;

- Mental mathematics can be planned so that, within an organised structure, it is possible to offer children enjoyment, challenge and success.

There are three teacher's guides in the series and they are designed to be used with children aged 5 to 7, 7 to 9 and 9 to 11 respectively, although many of the activities for one age range can easily be adapted for use with other age groups. The contents of the guides take into account the National Numeracy Framework, the requirements of the National Curriculum and the Scottish 5-14 Guidelines. Most of the ideas included in the teacher's guides have been trialled by class teachers who have helped to select activities which are both motivating and practical.

All three teacher's guides have the same structure. Each one is divided into three sections.

Section 1 provides brief guidelines for teachers on aspects of good practice to bear in mind when teaching mental mathematics. Ideas for effective classroom organisation, pupil participation, differentiation, assessment and interactive displays are also included in this section.

Section 2 provides structured practical ideas for the teacher to use with the whole class or groups. Specific skills for the teacher to focus on are highlighted. These ideas can be used as 'ten minuteses', as part of the 'numeracy hour', or can be extended for use in the main teaching session. Ideas for extension are suggested so that some activities can also be used over a period of time. Possible learning and reinforcement outcomes are listed, along with ways of introducing the activities, questions, list of resources and extensions.

Accompanying each teacher's page is a photocopiable activity sheet which relates to some of the skills addressed. The teacher's guide pages are cross-referenced to the pupil book pages.

Section 3 consists of more photocopiable activity sheets and games which children can use individually, in small groups or as part of a whole-class lesson. These sheets include activities which can be completed at the level specified by most children without much adult help. A collection of short puzzles and problem-solving activities are also included at the end of this section; these provide ideal opportunities for children to 'use' and 'apply' number. Many teachers have used these activities for whole-class teaching or for individual and pair work at the beginning or end of a lesson.

SECTION 1

USING THIS GUIDE TO TEACH MENTAL MATHEMATICS

All the ideas here encourage children to be actively involved in mental calculations. Some activities are to be undertaken without the aid of paper and pencil, counters or any physical objects. Others involve recording or being engaged in activities which demand a great deal of mathematical thinking and estimating skills. Jotting down ideas is necessary on some occasions where recording ideas helps children to extend their ideas further, to be involved in developing higher levels of thinking and to internalise more complex ideas. Particular attention is given to encouraging children to construct mental images to help them acquire a conceptual understanding of mathematical ideas.

The collection of ideas on each of the teacher's pages is intended to be used over an extended period of time. Teachers may, of course, use the simpler ideas within an activity with a group of children and return to the more advanced aspects after a period of time. The photocopiable sheets provide some ideas for recording; again, these can be adapted for extended use.

In selecting activities to be included in the guide, the following features were considered important:

- Motivating and meaningful contexts;
- Opportunities for practice and reinforcement;

- Possibilities for building mental imagery;
- Opportunities for oral work.

THE IMPORTANCE OF TEACHING MENTAL MATHEMATICS

The importance of children being able to do mental mathematics has always been recognised; the Cockcroft Report (1982), 'Mathematics 5-16' (HMI, 1985) and the National Curriculum have all made strong recommendations that children should develop effective strategies for mental calculations. International comparisons of children's mathematical competencies and the National Numeracy Project have brought the role of mental mathematics to the forefront of mathematics education.

Teachers recognise both the power children can derive from being 'good' at mental mathematics and their professional role in supporting children in achieving that objective. Everyone's ability at mental mathematics can be increased through structured activities and practice. This series offers guidance for that purpose.

Understanding concepts and being good at mental arithmetic go hand in hand in supporting each other. In order to encourage conceptual understanding of ideas which will enrich children's mental mathematics skills, the teacher needs to address the following:

- Provision of practical activities which help children to explore the nature and inter-relationships between numbers and of the number system.

- The use of number lines and structured materials to introduce and enhance children's understanding of concepts. The use of such materials should be to support children to develop mental imagery and strategies to work with numbers more effectively. Children should not be made to depend on them for longer than necessary.

- The need to be able to 'recall facts' – number bonds and table facts – quickly is effective and necessary, but understanding the principles behind these facts is also important. It makes it possible for children to tackle more complex applications of these facts by restructuring and adjusting what they know.

- The advantage of having short, regular mental maths sessions focusing on specific strategies. Without specific teaching, it is unlikely that children will develop the most efficient and economical methods of calculations. The use of 'child methods' may bring success in the short term; only systematic teaching is likely to make children develop effective strategies in the long term.

- The advantage of having regular sessions with specific emphasis on memorising facts.

DISCUSSION AND MENTAL MATHEMATICS

Effective teaching of mental mathematics will involve a considerable amount of oral work. Verbalising mathematical thinking enhances children's confidence. Listening to others makes them consider methods used by other people and their relative efficiency in order to refine their own thinking and methods.

Discussion during mental mathematics lessons may take many forms:

- The teacher introduces new ideas and demonstrates the ideas through clear explanations, inviting questions and clarifications from children. An interactive style of teaching will keep children actively involved in the learning process.

- Children are asked to share their methods, with the teacher structuring the discussions in such a way that all children's contributions are valued. These discussions can highlight the relative effectiveness of the methods used encouraging children to develop sensible strategies.

The types of questions which will elicit useful responses are: *'That was quick, tell me how you did it'*; *'Can you tell everyone how you did it?'*; *'If you were the teacher how would you explain it?'*; *'Tell the person next to you how you did this'*; *'That is great, I had never really thought about it that way'* and so on.

The sharing of methods can also be achieved through paired work. The children can ask each other mental maths problems and then probe how their partner tackled the calculations. They can then report back to the big group about the strategies used. Giving time to think before shouting out answers will help children to consider the 'reasonableness' of their responses and reflect on their methods.

- The quality of children's responses will most certainly depend on the type of questions asked. It is useful to remember that open-ended questions can bring a variety of answers which will help children to learn from each other.

- It is useful to discuss mistakes made by other 'imaginary' children in order to highlight misconceptions, errors and faulty strategies. For example, *'Daniel is working out 4 add 5 on the number line. He answered 8. Is the answer right? If not, what do you think Daniel might have done wrong?'* Responses may include that he probably started counting and included the 4: 4, 5, 6, 7, 8… and so on.

- The role of discussion in assessing children's learning is crucial. It is only through asking children probing questions and listening to their rationale for using different methods that teachers can plan the children's future learning and evaluate their own teaching.

ORGANISING THE CLASS FOR MENTAL ARITHMETIC

Conducting effective mental mathematics lessons requires a great deal of thinking and planning which makes it one of the most challenging aspects of a teacher's work.

The important issues to consider are **Differentiation**, **Grouping** and **Creating a 'Mental Maths' environment in the classroom**.

Differentiation

It is very likely that the 30 children in the class are at different stages in their mental mathematics development which makes differentiation an important aspect to consider. The following suggestions may help to achieve differentiation.

- When introducing an activity to the whole class, target the questions carefully so that some consideration is given to the children's level of ability to respond.

- Teach half or quarter of the class together for mental arithmetic whilst the other children work on a task introduced previously or something they can work on independently.

- Inviting children who put their hands up to respond is not always the most appropriate strategy. Ask children to keep their answers 'in their heads' until the teacher selects a person to answer a question.

- When asking for responses to the 'quick-fire' type of questions, encourage children to show their answers by holding up number cards when asked to do so. This enables the teacher to skim all the responses quickly.

- Encourage children to write down their answers individually as 'top secret' so the teacher can control how to deal with individual children's responses.

- Tell the children to have some thinking time before responding.

- After the introduction to the activity, get children to work in pairs or small groups with differentiated tasks. Extension ideas are provided in the teacher's guides.

- Use open-ended questions which will enable children to work at their level of ability.

Grouping

It makes sense to teach the whole group together when a new skill or idea is being introduced. For example, when the idea of doubling is introduced all children can be shown what it means. It also helps to tell children, in advance, what they are going to do and what is the purpose of an activity.

The importance of listening to each other and the need to have a quiet time when everyone is thinking, should be stressed. Give children opportunities to participate in different roles according to their capability and talent; for demonstrating ideas, volunteering to be players, explaining activities, recording on the number line, for score keeping and so on.

Small group work will be more appropriate when it is felt that children need to discuss ideas more thoroughly and make decisions which need more thinking and reflection. Ability grouping may be more appropriate for some tasks. The teacher may want to be present in one focused group for assessment purposes.

Mental maths activities can also be done in pairs or individually. The activity sheets, games and puzzles included in this book can be used for any of the above grouping styles.

Creating a 'Mental Maths' environment in the classroom

In order to succeed in teaching mental mathematics, it needs to be given a high profile. The following ideas have been found useful by practising teachers:

- Have a mental maths lesson at least four times a week. Short, well paced and focused '10 minute' lessons are sufficient. Some of these lessons may be used to introduce new ideas and others may be for testing what has been learnt or a combination of both.

- Focus on learning selected facts for the week such as learning two number facts or number bonds. *'Tell someone about these bonds'* or design a poster showing what the learnt number bonds mean.

- Have interactive displays in the classroom. For example, put up a question: *'The answer is 20, what are the questions?'* inviting children to put up their responses on strips of paper all week.

- Make 'counting times' special, using appropriate types of counting activities: rhymes, what number comes after 3, 29, 399 and so on.

- Have a regular 'close your eyes' time asking children to picture numbers, number lines, structured materials, calculations. Ask them to share what they see with others.

- Let children have their own number kits which contain number lines of different-sized numbers, blank lines for working things out, a collection of dice, sets of 0-9 number cards, their favourite number game and other materials which are useful at the time of teaching new ideas.

- Have a vocabulary book or display of useful words to learn and remember.

ASSESSING MATHEMATICAL LEARNING

Assessment of children's mental mathematics learning will normally be carried out by:

- listening to children's responses to direct questions, during discussions between the teacher and children or amongst children themselves;

- observing children working on tasks which require numerical recording;

- marking children's written responses to tasks on the pupil book pages.

The following questions will be useful to consider when assessing children's mental mathematics:

- Are children using the correct mathematical vocabulary?
- Can they recall useful number facts?
- Are they able to work accurately and with speed?
- Are they able to use taught strategies efficiently?
- Are there any misconceptions in pupils' understanding of ideas?

Diagnostic interviews with children will help to highlight the nature of any specific difficulties which can be dealt with.

STRATEGIES FOR DOING MENTAL ARITHMETIC

In general terms, the following strategies help to acquire competence in mental arithmetic.

- Instant recall of number facts.
- Using a fact from memory and making adjustments to use these facts in other situations.
- Rearranging numbers to make a calculation more manageable.
- Knowing doubles and halves.
- Using a mental number line.
- Using mental imagery developed through previous experiences.
- Estimating a possible solution.
- Splitting numbers into parts to make calculations easier. Using generalised rules of multiplying and dividing by 5s, 10s and 100s.

In the early years of schooling, with which this book is particularly concerned, stories, songs and rhymes provide the teacher with a wealth of opportunities for oral work on numbers and building images of numbers and number bonds. Songs such as 'Five freckled frogs' can be used to give a concrete representation of what would otherwise be abstract and remote to the children. Similarly, a visual aid chart based on the leaves eaten by 'The Hungry Caterpillar' (see page 12) each day of the week provides a meaningful context for mental calculations using addition bonds.

Counting forwards and backwards

RESOURCES

A floor number line, with numbers 0-10 clearly marked. Number lines 0-10 for children to use. Squared paper for children to make their own number lines

KEY LANGUAGE

number names, counting on, counting back, jumps, forwards, back, leaps, more than, less than

REFERENCES

Pupil Book 1: pages 2, 3, 4, 5

LEARNING OUTCOMES

- Counting forwards and backwards with numbers up to 10 using a number line first and then visualising the number line leading to instant recall.
- Learning the idea of using the first number as a 'marker' for both forward and backward jumps.

TEACHING NOTES

Freddie's number line

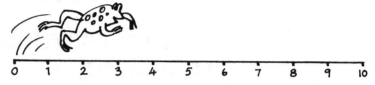

- Show children the floor number line and ask them to describe it, highlighting the following: the way the numbers are marked, the distances between numbers which are the same and the order in which the numbers appear.
- Ask the children: *'What number comes after 4; what are the two number neighbours of number 6?'* and so on. Such questions will support mental imagery.
- Get different children to pretend to be 'Freddie the Froggie' and walk along the number line saying: *'Stand on number 4, move forward 3, what is Freddie standing on now?... Count on 2 more, where is Freddie now?'* It is important to stress the role of the first number as a marker and move from there, as children often find the 'counting on' strategy difficult.
- Ask Freddie to count back now: *'Stand on 5, count back 4, where is he now?'*
- Without making the movements this time, say to the children: *'Freddie is standing on number 5, if he jumped 3 numbers forward, where will he land? What if he then jumped another 3?'* Emphasise and encourage the usefulness of instant recall.

EXTENSION ACTIVITIES

- Ask the children to close their eyes and picture in their minds a number line. Ask them questions such as: *'If you start on 4 and count on 3, what number will you land on? If you start on 8 and count back 2, what number will you be standing on?'*
- *'What number is 4 more than 5? 5 count on 3, 8 count back 0...'* and so on.
- Suggest that the children make their own number lines using animals of their choice. Ask the children to give each other mental tests of counting on and back.

Freddie's number line

Freddie can work out in his head where he will land on his number line for different numbers of jumps.

1. Use your mental number line to work out where Freddie will land. Complete the table.

STARTING NUMBER	NUMBER OF JUMPS AND DIRECTION	LANDING NUMBER
0	4 FORWARD	4
2	6 FORWARD	
3	5 FORWARD	
7	3 FORWARD	
10	5 BACKWARD	
4	5 FORWARD	
0	9 FORWARD	
5	5 FORWARD	
9	2 BACKWARD	

2. Work out the direction and number of jumps Freddie made to land on these numbers.

STARTING NUMBER	NUMBER OF JUMPS AND DIRECTION	LANDING NUMBER
4		7
10		6
8		6
7		3
5		9

Name _____   **Date** _____

Collins Mental Maths © HarperCollins*Publishers* Ltd 1998

Subtraction and addition of numbers to 10

RESOURCES
A cut-out of the caterpillar and sliding card on Resource master 1.

KEY LANGUAGE
number names 'one' to 'ten', take away, hidden, missing number

REFERENCES
Pupil Book 1: pages 5, 10, 13
Resource master 1

LEARNING OUTCOMES

- Subtraction and addition of numbers to ten.
- Mental imagery of numbers up to ten and missing number concept.

TEACHING NOTES
The hungry caterpillar

- Cut out the caterpillar and leaves on Resource master 1 (page 42). Fold along the dotted lines and glue the two sections to form a pocket.

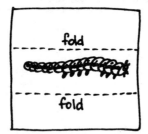 

- Show the children the picture of the caterpillar and the leaves. Ask them to count the leaves.
- Slide the leaves into the pocket behind the caterpillar, but leave three leaves showing. Say to the children: *'How many leaves has the caterpillar eaten?'*
- Ask the children to explain how they know it is 7, stressing the number bond 3 + 7 = 10.
- Repeat the activity with other combinations of numbers.
- Ask the children to suggest different ways of making ten.
- Write on the board:

$$4 + \square = 10$$
$$8 + \square = 10$$
$$1 + \square = 10 \text{ and so on.}$$

This activity can be continued, in groups, recording the story of ten.

EXTENSION ACTIVITIES

- Make a 'number kebab' by placing a fixed number of beads on a knitting needle. Secure both ends with Blu-Tack or plasticine and use the 'kebab' as a counting rod. Use it in the same way as the caterpillar.
- Spilt the beads of the kebab into three or four parts. Hide one or two sections and ask the children more complicated bonds: 4 (hidden) + 3 + 3 (hidden) = 10.
- You can make these activities more challenging by using larger numbers of leaves or beads.

Making 10s

1. Write numbers in the boxes to show
   how you can make 10 in different ways.

☐ + ☐ = 10   ☐ + ☐ = 10

☐ + ☐ = 10   ☐ + ☐ = 10

☐ + ☐ = 10   ☐ + ☐ = 10

☐ + ☐ = 10   ☐ + ☐ = 10

2. Tom has forgotten to put numbers and signs in these boxes.
   Complete the sums with these numbers: 2, 3, 4, 5.
   You can use the same numbers more than once.
   Write the add (+) and take away (−) signs.

| 3 | + | 2 | = 5 | | 6 | − | 3 | = 3 |

☐ ☐ ☐ = 1   ☐ ☐ ☐ = 6

☐ ☐ ☐ = 2   ☐ ☐ ☐ = 7

☐ ☐ ☐ = 3   ☐ ☐ ☐ = 8

☐ ☐ ☐ = 4   ☐ ☐ ☐ = 9

☐ ☐ ☐ = 5   ☐ ☐ ☐ = 10

Name _____   **Date** _____

Ordinal numbers

RESOURCES

Number labels 0-10 and 0-30, enough for the whole class to have two each. A number line marked 0-10 and another marked 0-30 for reference

KEY LANGUAGE

first, second, third...to tenth, order, more than, less than, same

REFERENCES

Pupil Book 1: pages 2, 3, 7, 23, 24

LEARNING OUTCOMES

- Conceptualisation of the ordinal aspect of numbers (the correct order in which they appear on a number line).
- Recognition of a number being greater than and less than other numbers.
- Vocabulary relating to first, second and so on.

TEACHING NOTES

- Stick a number label between 0 and 10 on the back of every child in the class. Ask them to find out what number is on their back by asking each other questions, for example: *'Is my number bigger than 3? less than 9? between 4 and 6?'* and so on. The answers can only be 'yes' or 'no'. They are not allowed to guess the number until they are nearly sure what the number is, and try to insist they can only have two turns to guess the number.
- When they have correctly guessed the number, they can collect another number label for sticking on the front of them.
- When everyone has collected their labels, ask them to try to make human number lines from 0-10. Check the human number lines are in order and whether any numbers are missing.
- Use the human number line to reinforce vocabulary: first, second, third, by describing the person with the specific number label. For example ask: *'In what position is the person wearing the blue, striped jumper standing?'* Children often find the vocabulary difficult and will need help and much practice to both understand the concept and to say the words.
- Let all the children sit down. Then ask just one human number line to stand in front of the class. Ask the children to look away while you swap two children and say: *'What is wrong with our number line?'* Change the order of more than two children and ask the children to spot what is wrong.
- While the other children close their eyes, ask one or two children in one of the 0-10 number lines to move away from the number line. Ask: *'What number/s is/are missing?'*

EXTENSION ACTIVITIES

- Use the number people to illustrate operations asking: *'Which two number people will add up to 10? 11? 13? 14?'*
- Let children have numbers from 0-30 on their backs and ask them to hold hands with the person who is two more than them. They will be surprised to see that two groups are formed. Repeat with three more than them, and so on.

Lucky dip

1.

Today is your lucky day.
Which bucket will you dip into for these toys?
Write the numbers in the boxes.

Boat ☐   Cat ☐

Teddy bear ☐   Dolls' clothes ☐

Ball ☐   Dice ☐

Toy car ☐   Horse ☐

2. These letters are all jumbled up.
Put them in the right order and write the letters in the boxes.

☐ ☐ ☐   ☐ ☐ ☐ ☐   ☐ ☐ ☐ ☐

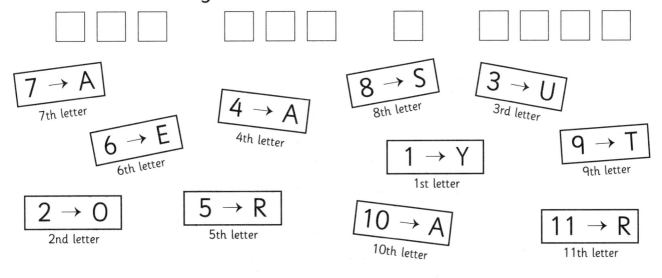

7 → A
7th letter

6 → E
6th letter

4 → A
4th letter

8 → S
8th letter

1 → Y
1st letter

3 → U
3rd letter

9 → T
9th letter

2 → O
2nd letter

5 → R
5th letter

10 → A
10th letter

11 → R
11th letter

Name _____   **Date** _____

Subtraction and addition of numbers to 20

RESOURCES

Three spotty dice marked 1-6 (larger dice are suitable for whole-class discussion)

KEY LANGUAGE

how many, add, total, difference, faces, opposite faces, subtract

REFERENCES

Pupil Book 1: pages 4, 5, 7, 10

LEARNING OUTCOMES

- Missing numbers, addition of numbers and working out differences.

TEACHING NOTES

- Show children a die and ask them if they know the special way the spots on it are arranged. Say: *'Do you know what the opposite faces add up to?'*
- Throw the die and ask the children to tell you what number is hidden. If children don't know the fact that opposite faces add up to 7, explain it to them. Repeat with different faces.
- Ask the children: *'What is the total number of spots on one die? Can you add them up quickly?'*
- Place one die on top of another and say to the children: *'Can you work out the number of spots on the 3 hidden faces?'*
- Arrange the dice sideways. Say: *'How many hidden spots are there?'* Try with 3 dice and hidden spots.
- Ask: *'How many spots are there altogether on 2 dice? 3 dice?'* Say: *'How many ways can you get a total of 12 with 3 dice and 18 with 4 dice?'*

EXTENSION ACTIVITIES

- Ask: *'What if I threw double 6 playing 2 dice, how many other spots will be showing?'*
- Suggest that the children do an addition square (see below) to show the totals for two dice throws, working out the scores mentally. Ask the children: *'What totals come up the most? the least? What is the highest number possible?'*

DICE 1

+	1	2	3	4	5	6
1	2	3	4	5	6	7
2	3	4	5	6	7	8
3	4	5	6	7	8	9
4	5	6	7	8	9	10
5	6	7	8	9	10	11
6	7	8	9	10	11	12

DICE 2

Ten pence sweets

Each sweet costs 10p.
Using only 1p, 2p and 5p coins, show how you could
pay for them in different ways.

Reordering numbers

RESOURCES
Counters or beans,
two dice marked 0-5,
grids marked with all
possible totals of two
dice, 0-9 cards

KEY LANGUAGE
add, plus, total,
altogether, rearrange,
reorder

REFERENCES
Pupil Book 1: pages 4,
5,10

LEARNING OUTCOMES

- Adding a string of numbers.
- Understanding that when adding two numbers, it is more efficient to reorder the numbers by putting the larger number first. For example, when adding 1 + 3, rearrange the numbers as 3 + 1 and then add them together.

TEACHING NOTES

- Show the whole class two sets of beans or counters, one set has three counters and the other set has six. Ask the children to add the two groups of counters and find the total. Now reverse the order of the groups of counters and ask for the total. Are the answers the same? Ask the children how they added the numbers. The teaching point is to highlight the efficiency of reordering the two digits with the larger first. Stress that when adding the two numbers six and three, the answer is the same whichever order they are added.
- Ask some 'quick-fire' addition sums 3 + 8, 7 + 3, 4 + 5, 3 + 1 + 2 and so on, encouraging the reordering strategy.
- Play a two dice game in teams or with two volunteers as follows. Each player has some counters and a board marked with all the numbers obtained by throwing two dice marked 1 to 5. In turn, each player rolls the dice and adds up the scores. They then cover the total on the board. The player who has covered all the squares or the most number of squares wins. Emphasise both the reordering strategy and the way the game can help them to memorise and recall number bonds.
- Send the children away to play the game in pairs or small groups. Tell them that you will test to see if the game has helped their recall of number bonds when they come back together.

EXTENSION ACTIVITIES

- Make up an addition square of 5.
- Ask: 'What numbers can you make if the dice are marked 1-6?'
- Ask: 'How would you reorder three numbers: 2 + 5 + 1 to find their totals?'
- Get children, in turn, to choose three cards from the pack of 0-9 number cards. Show the cards to the class and ask the others to add them up mentally. For example, a child may pick 2, 5 and 1 and the need to rearrange the numbers can be highlighted. Repeat with four cards.

Add them up

Use the numbers below to make these sums correct.
You can use the numbers more than once.

| 5 | 1 | 2 | 6 | 7 | 8 | 9 | 3 | 2 |

☐ + ☐ = 4   ☐ + ☐ = 3

☐ + ☐ = 6   ☐ + ☐ = 10

☐ + ☐ = 9   ☐ + ☐ = 7

☐ + ☐ = 8   ☐ + ☐ = 5

Try each of these in two different ways.

☐ + ☐ + ☐ = 7   ☐ + ☐ + ☐ = 7

☐ + ☐ + ☐ = 6   ☐ + ☐ + ☐ = 6

☐ + ☐ + ☐ = 5   ☐ + ☐ + ☐ = 5

☐ + ☐ + ☐ =10   ☐ + ☐ + ☐ = 10

Name _____   **Date** _____

Doubling numbers

RESOURCES
Inter-locking cubes, dice, dominoes, number lines

KEY LANGUAGE
add, plus, sum, double, half, split, together

REFERENCES
Pupil Book 2: pages 8, 10

LEARNING OUTCOMES

- The concept of doubling a number, calculating and practising doubling of numbers.
- Awareness of the efficiency of the doubling strategy for mental calculations.

TEACHING NOTES

Double power

- Show the children two dice marked 1-6 and say to them: '*How many doubles can you see?*'
- Using the inter-locking cubes, ask the children to make a double which is bigger than the double on the dice.
- Choose children to come to the front of the class and ask them to place the dominoes into two sets: 'doubles' and 'not doubles'.
- On a board or a flip chart, ask the children to find these doubles:

$$1 + 1 = 2$$
$$2 + 2 = 4$$
$$3 + 3 = 6$$

Go up to a total of 10.

- Show the children a number line. Say to them: '*What pattern do you notice?*' '*What is special about these numbers?*'
- Ask the children to pick out some more 'doubles' on the number line. '*What two numbers do you have to double to get that number?*'
- Read out these numbers to the children: 8, 14, 21, 40, 45, 66, 100. They should work out the **whole number** which is doubled to get each number. Tell them to call out if they think that you have tried to trick them with any of the numbers.
- Now try some 'quick quiz' questions. Say to the children, '*What is double 4, double 10, double 22...?*' Pick children who are able to handle the number you choose. Offer challenging numbers for the more able children.
- This could be followed by sending children to their seats to write down some 'doubled' numbers.

EXTENSION ACTIVITIES

- Ask more questions about doubles:
  '*Can you tell me what "half" of a number means?*'; '*How is a "double" and a "half" related?*'; '*What is half of 4? 8? 40? 100?*'; '*Tell me the largest number you can double; then say the answer.*'; '*How can you use the idea of doubling to add other numbers which are near doubles?*' Ask the children to work out these: 4 + 5; 7 + 8; 11 + 12; 25 + 26; 50 + 52.
- Suggest making a book or display of 'double' facts. The children can add to the collection whenever they think of a new fact.

Double power

1. This ladybird wants to have the same number of spots on both sides so that the total number of spots is a double. The numbers 2 and 4 will work because they are doubles and can be split into two equal sets.

Write down six numbers which will work and make the ladybird happy.

_____

2. Look at these numbers and draw a ring round the doubles.

| 8 | 13 | 5 | 18 | 22 | 19 | 98 |

| 68 | 20 | 40 | 78 | 91 | 43 | 36 |

| 79 | 29 | 84 | 29 | 81 | 82 |

Name _____ **Date** _____

Collins Mental Maths © HarperCollins*Publishers* Ltd 1998

Near doubles

RESOURCES

Cards with sums which involve adding doubles: 3 + 3, 6 + 6, 10 + 10. Cards with sums which involve adding near doubles: 3 + 4, 6 + 7, 12 + 13. Cards with sums which involve larger numbers and adding near doubles: 30 + 29, 40 + 38, 50 + 49 where doubling and taking away 1 or 2 can be used as a strategy

KEY LANGUAGE

double, near double, add, plus, take away, minus, subtract

REFERENCES

Pupil Book 1: page 19
Pupil Book 2: page 10

LEARNING OUTCOMES

- Recognising near doubles of numbers, such as a difference of one when adding numbers, for example, 6 + 7, or 40 + 39, and then adjusting.

TEACHING NOTES

- Remind children about doubles which they have encountered previously. Ask them in turn to list all the doubles they know. Write some of these down on the board or a flip chart.
- Tell the children they are going to look at near doubles of numbers to see how they can help to calculate numbers.
- Write sums such as 6 + 7, 8 + 9, 3 + 4 on the flip chart and ask children if they can use their double facts to work them out. Encourage them to verbalise strategies as much as possible. Stress the fact that '7 is one more than 6' and '9 is one more than 8'; so double 6 plus 1 will give you the answer to 6 + 7. Repeat with different numbers.
- Ask the children if they find knowing 'doubles' is useful in working out 9 + 8, 9 + 7 and so on. The strategy double 9 minus 1, double 9 minus 2 may need to be pointed out to children if they don't suggest it.
- Point out that 'tens' numbers are easier to double. Say to the children: 'Can we use the near doubles strategy to add 10 + 11, 20 + 22, 40 + 41?' and so on. 'What about 20 + 19, 30 + 28, 30 + 29?'
- Send the children away to work in pairs or groups to add as many number 'neighbours' (6 + 7, 6 + 5, 20 + 21, 9 + 8) as possible in five minutes using the near double strategy.

EXTENSION ACTIVITIES

- Ask the children to use larger numbers to add near doubles.
- Try the near doubles strategy for adding 102 + 104.
- Put up a display of how to use 'near doubles' to add numbers more efficiently.
- The children could ask some adults to add near double numbers and find out if they use the same method.
- Ask children to design a poster of a machine which will identify near doubles and demonstrate how it works. For example, the machine will identify:

$$29 + 30 \quad \text{as} \quad 30 + 30 = 60 - 1$$
$$\text{or} \quad 29 + 29 = 58 - 1$$

$$60 + 61 \quad \text{as} \quad 60 + 60 = 120 + 1$$
$$\text{or} \quad 61 + 61 = 122 - 1$$

Double help

1. Fill in the addition square.
Draw a red ring round all the numbers you got by doubling a number. One of the doubles is shown.

+	1	2	3	4	5	6	7	8	9	10
1										
2										
3										
4										
5										
6						(12)				
7										
8										
9										
10										

2. Use the double facts to help you to add these near doubles.

2+2+1= ☐   3+3+1= ☐   5+5+1= ☐   4+4+1= ☐

6+6+1= ☐   7+7+1= ☐   9+9+1= ☐   8+8+1= ☐

3+4= ☐   7+6= ☐   4+5= ☐   6+7= ☐

5+4= ☐   5+6= ☐   4+3= ☐   8+9= ☐

10+11= ☐   9+8= ☐   6+5= ☐   11+10= ☐

Name _____   **Date** _____

Making 20

RESOURCES

Number line, score sheets and four sets of cards with numbers 0-16

KEY LANGUAGE

add, how many more, total, nearest, goes over the target

REFERENCES

Pupil Book 1: pages 7, 14, 23
Pupil Book 2: pages 9, 21, 22

LEARNING OUTCOMES

- Adding three numbers to obtain totals of 20 or near 20. Using a number line to check nearness, the difference between numbers up to 20.

TEACHING NOTES

Twenty win

- Invite three volunteer players to demonstrate the game at the front of the class. Shuffle the number cards and place the pile face down.
- Player A takes the top card and displays the card open for everyone to see – say it is number four. Players B and C do the same. Explain that the objective of the game is for each player to take three cards and add them up to get as near as possible to 20. Decide the rules for scoring, for example, if the player gets exactly 20 they get three points, one less or more on either side – 21 and 19 – wins two points. If it is two less or more on either side, they score one point.

> **Score sheet**
> 3 points for exact 20
> 2 points for 19 or 21
> 1 point for 18 or 22
>
> | Melanie | Rishma | Darren |
> |---------|--------|--------|
> | 1 | 1 | 0 |
> | 1 | 0 | 3 |

- In the second round, the players add the new number to the first number. For example, if player A has the number 10, they now have 14 so far, 6 more to go to get a 20.
- When all three players have added up their three cards, discuss whose score is the nearest to 20. All calculations are to be done mentally. If player A got an 8 for round three, the total will be 22. If the three players' totals are A: 22, B: 21 and C: 19, then their scores are A: 1, B: 2 and C: 2.
- Play a few times and add up the scores.

EXTENSION ACTIVITIES

- List all the different ways of getting a total of 20.
- Change the scoring system to five points for exact 20, and so on.
- Change the target number to 30 or higher.

Target twenty

1. You have four dice all marked 1 to 6. Imagine you are rolling them altogether and adding up the scores.

- How many different ways can you get a score of 20?
- Write the four numbers in each throw which give a total of 20.

$$\boxed{} + \boxed{} + \boxed{} + \boxed{} = 20$$

2. Imagine you have five dice. Write the five numbers in each throw which give a total of 20.

$$\boxed{} + \boxed{} + \boxed{} + \boxed{} + \boxed{} = 20$$

Name _____ **Date** _____

Counting in tens and units

RESOURCES

Ten sticks made from inter-locking cubes and single bricks. Feely bags to hide the blocks and units

KEY LANGUAGE

tens, units, blocks, remove, add, subtract, how many, counting in tens, total

REFERENCES

Pupil Book 1: pages 8, 13, 14
Pupil Book 2: pages 2, 4, 9, 16, 18, 19

LEARNING OUTCOMES

- Understanding the structure of tens and units in our number system.
- Counting in tens and in tens and units.
- Adding and subtracting tens and tens and units mentally.

TEACHING NOTES

Tens in bags

- Remind children about tens and units and the equivalence of one ten and ten units.
- Put out three ten blocks and four ones and ask them to tell you how many there are. Encourage the children to count in tens – 10, 20, 30 and then 31, 32, 33, 34. Sometimes there is a tendency for children to count in tens and then carry on counting the units in tens without thinking!
- Ask two volunteers to come to the front of the class to demonstrate the activity. Give each child five ten blocks and ten units to put in their feely bags, making sure that everyone in the class has also seen the contents going into the bags.
- The first child takes two tens out of the bag and the others work out how many are left in the bag. Discuss the strategies used. The tens are then returned to the bag. The second child repeats the activity, this time taking out three tens and four units. The two children play a few more times, removing tens and units and asking others to guess how many are left.
- *'I have taken two tens and six units. I am taking three more units out. How many are left?'*
- Ask the children to close their eyes and listen: *'My bag is empty. I put in three tens, seven units and another four units, what do I have now? What do you see?'* This can be repeated with subtraction: *'I start with four tens, I put in three tens and five units. I then take away nine units'* and so on.

EXTENSION ACTIVITIES

- Increase the size of numbers by starting with more tens. Start with a hundred block and some ten blocks.
- When one child is adding or removing the blocks, let others write down how many are left in the bag.

Bunches of flowers

A bunch of ten flowers   A single flower

1. How many flowers are there in:

2 bunches? _____*20 flowers*_____

4 bunches? _____

6 bunches and 1 single? _____

5 bunches and 9 singles? _____

5 bunches and 3 singles? _____

8 bunches and 5 singles? _____

2. How many bunches can you make from:

42 flowers? ___4___ bunches and ___2___ singles

35 flowers? _____ bunches and _____ singles

72 flowers? _____ bunches and _____ singles

3. How many flowers are left?

4 bunches take away 5 flowers _____*35 flowers*_____

5 bunches take away 7 flowers _____

7 bunches take away 2 flowers _____

Name _____   **Date** _____

Adding, subtracting and multiplying

RESOURCES

Number line 0-100, sum dials stuck on to card (Resource master 2)

KEY LANGUAGE

add, subtract, plus, minus, times, total

REFERENCES

Pupil Book 1: page 15, 17
Pupil Book 2: page 21 (The idea can be adapted to many of the ideas in Book 2)
Resource master 2

LEARNING OUTCOMES

- Practice with adding and subtracting can be extended to multiplying numbers.

TEACHING NOTES

Sum dials

- Cut out the sum dials on the resource master and stick them on to card. Fasten the circles together with a brass paper fastener in order to allow easy movement. The two sections line up to provide eight sums at each movement.
- Before using sum dials to practise any operation, discuss with children what the operation means. It may be necessary to use counters, cubes and number lines in order to activate mental strategies and possible mental images.
- Ask children to come to the front of the class, in turn, and operate the dials whilst the others work out the sum mentally and respond quickly. The 64 sums available for each dial make them very useful for practice.
- Discuss strategies used by the children for the operation chosen and any mental imagery which helped them to do the calculation. This activity can continue in small groups.

EXTENSION ACTIVITIES

- Use larger numbers on the dials. These dials are versatile and very popular amongst children.
- Use more complex concepts: multipication, division, fractions, using suitable dials.
- Let children make dials and take them home. Ask them to bring in a list of number bonds they have mastered.
- Use sum dials with three circles and practise:
  – adding three numbers;
  – mixed operations.

The missing key

Can you help? I am using a
calculator to do these sums, but
I have a problem. The 6 key on
my calculator is missing.
Can you help me to choose
other keys to do these sums?

Work with a partner. You must discuss and agree your
answers before you write them down.

Sums	Keys to use	Answer
6 + 2	2 + 4 + 2	8
6 - 2		
16 + 5		
66 - 35		
16 + 16		
40 - 16		
6 x 2		
26 - 19		
6 x 10		
26 + 36		
72 + 60		

Name _____ **Date**_____

Odd and even numbers

RESOURCES

A laminated number line 0-100, washable pens to put marks on the number line, inter-locking cubes

KEY LANGUAGE

odd, even, number neighbour, in twos, pattern, jumps

REFERENCES

Pupil Book 1: pages 9, 11, 18
Pupil Book 2: pages 3, 8, 10

LEARNING OUTCOMES

- Conceptual understanding of odd and even numbers and relating them to number patterns on a number line.
- Practice of mental addition of a string of numbers.
- Using generated number patterns and rules to predict what will happen with larger numbers.

TEACHING NOTES

Neighbours

- Ask a group of children to make towers using the inter-locking cubes, to represent numbers in order: 1, 2, 3, 4, 5, 6, 7, 8 and 9.
- Ask the children: *'Which inter-locking cube towers can you share into two equal sets (into equal halves)?'* The children can then mark those numbers on the number line. Say to the children: *'Try to split one into two sets – it can't be done – try two and mark it on the number line. Keep going.'* What do the children notice about the number line? Discuss the emerging pattern. All the numbers which are marked are even numbers and the others are odd numbers. Say to the children: *'Is 20 odd or even? 24? 21?'*
- *'What can you say about odd and even numbers as number neighbours?'*
- With the whole class listening and watching, ask the children to choose pairs of number neighbours (1 + 2, 3 + 4, 5 + 6,) and add them up. Mark the total on the number line. What do the children notice?
- Ask the children to predict whether the total of three consecutive numbers will be odd or even; whether it will really depend on which kind of number you start with will be an exciting discovery.

EXTENSION ACTIVITIES

- In small groups, ask the children to try four number neighbours.
- Suggest that the children try to make all the numbers from 1 to 20 adding consecutive numbers. They can make up a table with information such as: you can make 1 by adding 0 + 1, you cannot make 2, you can make 3 by adding 1 + 2, you cannot make 4, and so on.
- Make a book of 'Facts about number neighbours'.

Snakes

1. The segments of these snakes grow in a special way.
Start with the number on the head.
If it is an **odd** number, add 1 to it.
If it is an **even** number, halve it.
The snake keeps growing until you reach number 1.

This snake has number 5 on its head.
See how the segments grow.

Now try these.

Which head number gives you the longest snake? _____

2. Which of the following numbers will give you
the longest snake?
Guess the answer first and then find out by drawing
them on the back of this sheet.

18   17   20

Name _____ **Date** _____

Addition of a string of numbers

RESOURCES

Prepare two money alphabet strips from Resource master 2 for the whole class to see. Instead of assigning money values, scores can be used, if preferred

KEY LANGUAGE

add, total, sum, value, highest, lowest, difference, worth

REFERENCES

Pupil Book 1: pages 17, 26
Pupil Book 2: pages 16, 18, 19, 21
Resource master 2

LEARNING OUTCOMES

- Mental addition of a string of numbers using a range of strategies, estimation, difference, ordering numbers.

TEACHING NOTES

Alphabet's worth

- Ask children to add a string of numbers mentally, for example, $6 + 13 + 4 + 1$. Repeat a few times.
- Discuss the appropriate money alphabet with the children, highlighting what each letter is worth. Often children feel more motivated using money scores!
- Pick a word, for example, 'CAT' and ask the children to work out mentally what it is worth: $3 + 1 + 10 = 14$. Share strategies used for adding up and their efficiency.
- Ask selected children: *'What is your favourite animal? What is it worth? Whose animal is worth the highest? lowest?'*
- Keep asking targeted questions: *'Can you think of an animal which is worth exactly 100?'* Ask the children to find the most valuable word and share their word's worth with other children's words.
- Ask questions such as: *'Which word gives you the higher score ORANGE or BANANA? Think of a fruit which is worth exactly 20.'*
- In pairs or groups, work out words mentally (only jotting down is allowed). Get them to find out which words are worth more than a specified score, worth exactly a given score, a living animal with the highest score, and so on.
- In plenary discussions it is important to point out the efficient use of strategies for adding up.

EXTENSION ACTIVITIES

- Use the alphabet with values from 1 to 26 to provide extension to bigger numbers.
- Ask the children to estimate what selected words are worth without adding them up.
- Give a score and ask children to work out which flower or piece of furniture you are thinking of.
- Organise a display entitled 'Alphabet's Worth' where children can pin up words worth between 20–30, 40–50, 50–100. Display challenges such as: *'Pin up the name of an animal worth...'* *'an insect worth...'* and so on, for an interactive maths project.

What's it worth?

ABCDEFGHIJKLMNOPQRSTUVWXYZ
1 2 3 4 5 6 7 8 9 10 11 12 13 14 15 16 17 18 19 20 21 22 23 24 25 26

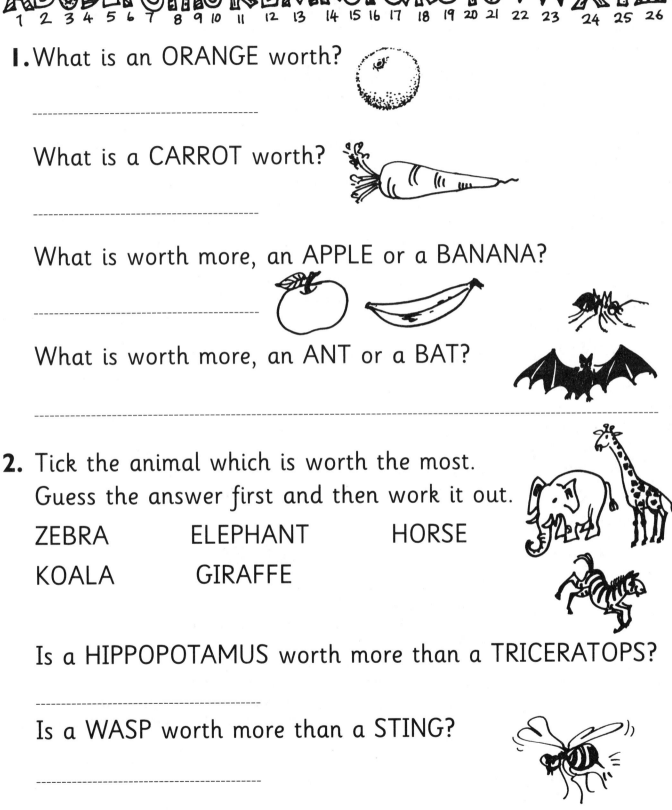

1. What is an ORANGE worth?

What is a CARROT worth?

What is worth more, an APPLE or a BANANA?

What is worth more, an ANT or a BAT?

----

2. Tick the animal which is worth the most.
Guess the answer first and then work it out.

ZEBRA   ELEPHANT   HORSE

KOALA   GIRAFFE

Is a HIPPOPOTAMUS worth more than a TRICERATOPS?

Is a WASP worth more than a STING?

Name _____ **Date** _____

Tens numbers

LEARNING OUTCOMES

- Emphasising tens numbers.
- Adding and subtracting using the tens knowledge.
- Carrying out calculations which involve 'bridging' across tens and making numbers either to or back to the nearest ten.

TEACHING NOTES

Maths machine 1

- Get a volunteer child to come to the front and mark the tens numbers – 10, 20, 30 – on the number line while the rest of the class chant tens numbers to 100.
- Ask the children to use the number line to help them to add numbers: 10 + 10, 30 + 20 and so on.
  Explain how to add 9 or 19. When adding 12 + 9, add 12 + 10 and take away 1. When adding 54 + 19, add 20 to 54 and take away 1.
- Say to the children, *'How would you add 47 + 64? Add the tens first and then the units?'* When adding 47 + 64, explain the usefulness of bridging through to the next ten. 47 is close to 50, so take it up to 50, add 61 (64 – 3), which equals 111. 50 + 60 (3 more and 4 less, so add 1) = 111.
- Introduce the maths machine. The machine can add any number fast and accurately. Stick selected labels on the machine, for example, *'Add 10'*, *'Add 20'* *'Add 9'* *'Add 19'* and so on. Ask a child to be manager of the machine and get other children to take it in turns to feed in an input card. Invite other children to calculate the result mentally. Another set of cards should be laid out next to the machine and the manager must pick out and show the correct output card. Change labels according to what operation is being practised.

EXTENSION ACTIVITIES

- Use a variety of operation labels for addition, subtraction, multiplication or division.
- Increase the complexity of the operations.
- Suggest that the children design 'calculating machines', operation cards and input and output numbers. Ask them to explain to the rest of the class how their machines work. Test the machines by getting the class to try different questions.
- Ask for volunteer 'human machines' for other children to ask mental questions.

Fast and fun

Imagine you are a very
fast adding up machine.
Complete these tables.

1.

Input number	Number to add	Output number
20	20	40
20	30	
7	30	
28	9	
30	19	
47	11	
37	21	
48	21	
57	31	
79	13	
39	35	

1.

Input number	Number to subtract	Output number
50	20	30
60	20	
50	9	
60	11	
70	21	
80	19	
64	15	
54	19	
90	28	

Name _____ **Date** _____

Ordering numbers up to 100

RESOURCES

Sets of 0-9, 0-40 and 0-100 number cards for the different levels of the activity, number lines 0-100, cubes, boards for four players to play at the same time (see Resource master 4)

KEY LANGUAGE

more than, less than, greater than, smaller than, between, odd, even, in the times table of, multiple, factors, 'square' number

REFERENCES

Pupil Book 1: pages 7, 21, 22, 23, 28
Pupil Book 2: pages 3, 4, 5, 17, 25, 26, 27
Resource master 4

LEARNING OUTCOMES

- Ordering numbers up to 100.
- Recognising odd and even numbers.
- Reinforcing multiplication tables of 2, 3, 5, 4 and 10.

TEACHING NOTES

Number friends

- Demonstrate the activity to the whole class by having two volunteers play the game or play in two teams with large boards.
- Place the appropriate set of shuffled cards face down in the centre. Give each player a board. Discuss with the children what the words on the board mean using the number line and cubes to demonstrate ideas.
- It is useful to introduce children to words such as 'multiple', 'factors', and 'square' numbers as early as possible so that they can internalise and use the concepts when opportunities arise.
- Each player takes a card from the pile in the middle and reads out the card. A decision is made where to place the card. For example, if the chosen card is 6 it can be placed on different positions: 'Even', 'Between 4 and 9' on the level 1 board. The number 36 can be placed on 'Square number', 'Multiple of 4', 'Even', 'Less than 85' on the level 3 board. Once a card is placed it cannot be moved. The winner is the first one to complete the board.
- Discuss efficient choice strategies. For example, a square number is more difficult to pick than a number between 28 and 65.

EXTENSION ACTIVITIES

- Use boards with an increased list of number properties.
- Ask the children to make a book of facts about chosen numbers. For example, 16 is a square number, it is in the tables of 2 and 4, it is between 10 and 18.
- Ask the children to make up other challenging boards.
- Ask the children to investigate which numbers from 1 to 100 have the most factors.
- Make up a chart showing collections of numbers which have the same amount of factors.

Secret numbers

Can you work out my secret numbers?

1. My number is lower than 30. It is higher than 15.
   It is an even number.
   The 2 digits of the number add up to 8.
   My number is _____

2. My number is higher than 25. It is lower than 50. If you
   count in 4s, 5s or in 10s from 0, you will land on me.
   My number is _____

3. My number is an odd number.
   It is less than 40. It is in the times table of 3.
   If you count in 9s from 0 you will land on me.
   My number is _____

4. My number is greater than 40. It is less than 100.
   It is close to 10 lots of 4. It is an odd number.
   If you add the digits you will think of the fingers of
   one of your hands.
   My number is _____

With a partner, make up three secret numbers.
Use a number line to make sure that your clues are perfect.

Name _____   **Date** _____

Collins Mental Maths © HarperCollins Publishers Ltd 1998

The relationship between multiplication and division

RESOURCES
Different versions of blank machines (see Resource master 3), stick-on labels or blank cards and Blu-tack

KEY LANGUAGE
multiply, times, share, input, output, divide

REFERENCES
Pupil Book 2: pages 25, 26, 27
Resource master 3

LEARNING OUTCOMES
- Reinforcement of multiplication.
- The concept of factors.
- The relationship between multiplication and division.

TEACHING NOTES
Maths machine 2
- Use the simple version (1) of the maths machine to explain how it works. The machine operates on the input number according to signs given as instructions. Discuss examples using addition, subtraction, multiplication and division.
- Remind children of the relationship between multiplication and division which they have learnt previously. Check: 'When you know that $2 \times 5 = 10$, you also know that $10 \div 2 = 5$ and $10 \div 5 = 2$.' If necessary, use counters to demonstrate this.
- Invite children to give multiplication facts and the division facts they can generate from it.
- Introduce the second version (2) of the maths machine on the board to the whole class. This machine can do two operations: add and subtract or multiply and divide. Explain how the machine works and about inputs and outputs.
- Ask why the input and output numbers are the same for the second machine, first using a simple example of adding and taking away, then show examples of multiplication and division.
- Write the input and output numbers in the machines and select children to write on the stick-on labels the multiplication and division operations. The children can then stick the numbers in the spaces.
- Ask if they can operate the third machine (3) which can do more operations. Vary the challenges for children: give the input number, output number and one operation and leave them to fill in the rest; give two operations and the output number and leave the input number blank.

EXTENSION ACTIVITIES
- Vary the complexity of the machines by using more functions and mixed operations.
- Control the size and type of numbers.
- Use blanks for children to fill in.

Magic loops

Remind yourself about the relationship between multiplication and division facts.

$$2 \times 4 = 8$$
so $8 \div 4 = 2$
$$8 \div 2 = 4$$

1. These are magic loops. Fill in the circles.

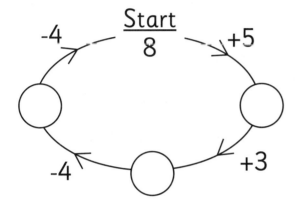 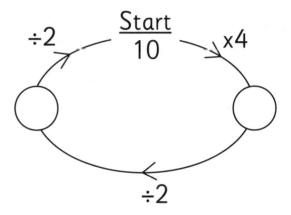

Explain why these work. _____

_____

_____

2. Draw some more magic loops using the multiplication and division facts you know.

Name _____ **Date** _____

Collins Mental Maths © HarperCollins Publishers Ltd 1998

Fractions: $\frac{1}{2}$, $\frac{1}{3}$, $\frac{1}{4}$

RESOURCES

Fraction boards, number lines for marking halves, quarters and thirds, blank number lines

KEY LANGUAGE

divided into equal parts, halves, quarters, thirds, halfway between

REFERENCES

Pupil Book 2: page 29

LEARNING OUTCOMES

- Development of imagery to acquire the fraction concept.
- Ability to use an internalised concept of fractions ($\frac{1}{2}$, $\frac{1}{3}$, $\frac{1}{4}$) in a variety of situations without the aid of pictures and written algorithms.

TEACHING NOTES

- Ask the children to respond to the questions: *'When I say the word "half" what do you see? a quarter? a third? two quarters?'* Ask them to verbalise what they see. Encourage them to come to the front and draw a picture of their ideas. It is important to emphasise the 'division' aspect of fractions and that half does not always mean one whole cut into two.
- Ask children to mark a half, a quarter and a third on the number line. Highlight that a half is the same as two quarters.
- Ask 12 children to come to the front of the class to demonstrate fractions. Get them to group into halves, quarters, thirds, two quarters, two thirds and so on.
- Ask questions such as: *'What is half of 6, 12, 24, 9, 32? a quarter of 8, 12, 16? two quarters of eight?' 'If two apples are shared equally between four people, what will each person get?' 'Which is a bigger piece of a chocolate – a quarter or a third? two quarters or half?'*

EXTENSION ACTIVITIES

- Ask questions using larger numbers.
- Extend the idea to other fractions: a tenth, eighth, sixth and so on.
- Suggest that the children design a track game involving the use of two dice and using money and fractions.
- Organise groups to make 'snap' cards to illustrate different fractions; for example $\frac{1}{2}$, $\frac{2}{4}$, $\frac{3}{6}$ are all different versions of half. Play 'fraction snap' with cards made.

Which bit?

1. Mark a $\frac{1}{2}$ on these number lines.

2. Mark a $\frac{1}{4}$ on these number lines.

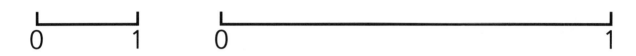

3. Mark a third $\frac{1}{3}$ on these number lines.

4. Tick the larger amount in each pair.

A half of 12p   A third of 15p

A quarter of 16p   A half of 24p

A third of 30p   A half of 36p

A third of 60p   A quarter of 88p

A quarter of 40p   A half of 50p

Name _____   **Date** _____

Resource master 1

THE HUNGRY CATERPILLAR (page 12)

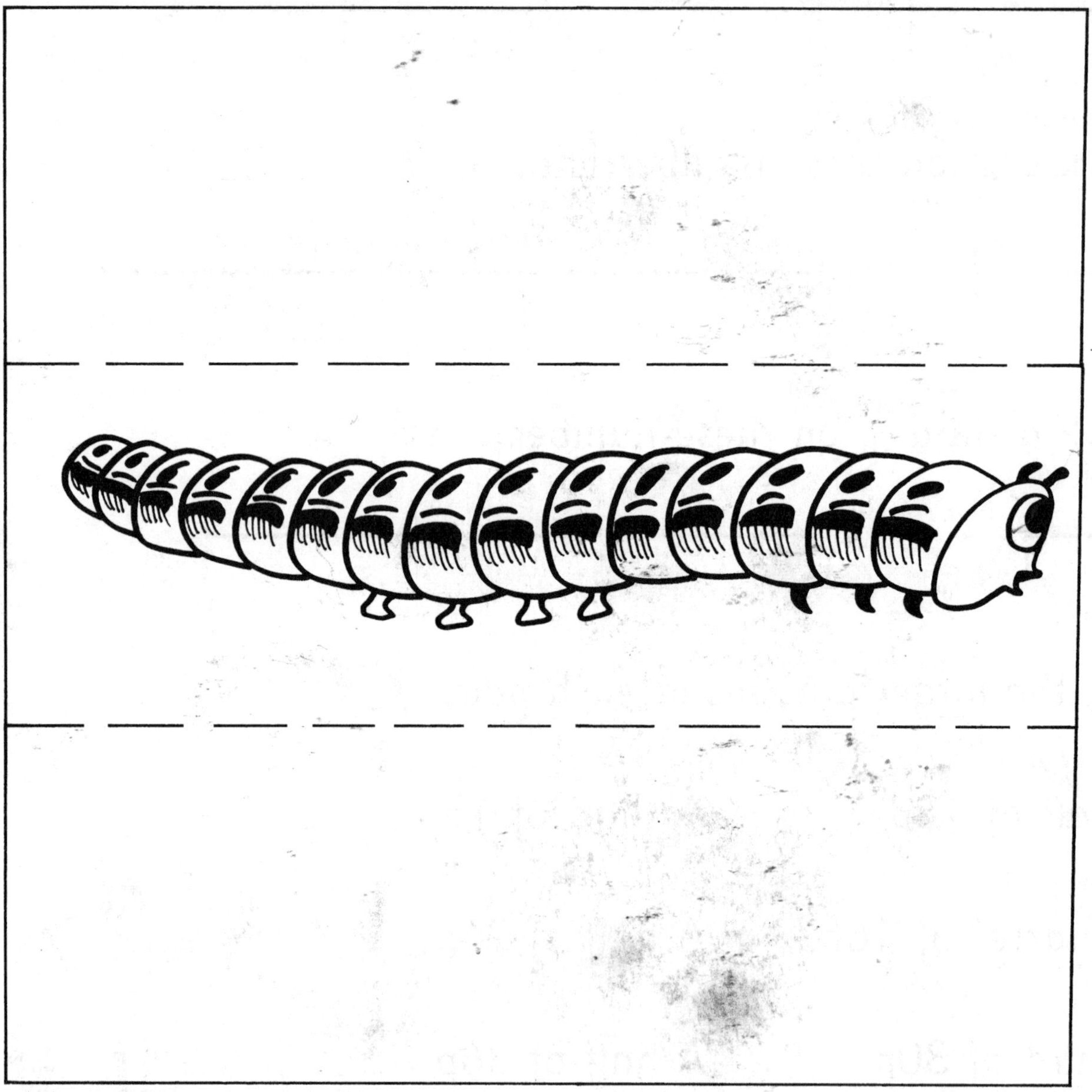

← Fold

← Fold

Resource master 2

SUM DIAL (page 28)

- Write numbers on the dial, positioned appropriately for mental calculations to be practised.
- Vary the signs as needed: + − x.
- To add and take away tens numbers, mark the outer ring: 10, 20, 30, 40, 50, 60, 70, 80 and the inner ring: 1, 2, 3, 4, 5, 6, 7, 8.

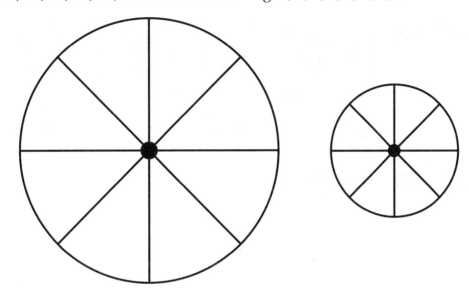

ALPHABET'S WORTH (page 32)

A	B	C	D	E	F	G	H	I	J	K	L	M
1p	2p	3p	4p	5p	6p	7p	8p	9p	10p	1p	2p	3p

N	O	P	Q	R	S	T	U	V	W	X	Y	Z
4p	5p	6p	7p	8p	9p	10p	1p	2p	3p	4p	5p	6p

A	B	C	D	E	F	G	H	I	J	K	L	M
1p	2p	3p	4p	5p	6p	7p	8p	9p	10p	11p	12p	13p

N	O	P	Q	R	S	T	U	V	W	X	Y	Z
14p	15p	16p	17p	18p	19p	20p	21p	22p	23p	24p	25p	26p

Resource master 3

MATHS MACHINE 1 (page 34)

MATHS MACHINE 2 (page 38)

Resource master 4

NUMBER FRIENDS (page 36)

1.

Between 6 and 9	Odd	Greater than 5	Even
More than 3	Less than 7	Smaller than 4	Between 4 and 9

2.

Between 10 and 30	Odd	Greater than 35	Less than 21
Even	In the times table of 4	Multiple of 3	More than 23

3.

Odd	Multiple of 4	Even	Higher than 60
Smaller than 31	Between 28 and 65	Less than 85	Multiple of 2 and 3

Activities, games and puzzles

In this section more activities, games and puzzles are provided. The primary objectives of this section are to encourage children to:

- practise their mental arithmetic skills;
- provide meaningful contexts for carrying out mental calculations and appreciating the importance of mental recall;
- be involved in mathematical thinking and reasoning;
- realise the role of systematic work in mathematics;
- be involved in oral communication of mental mathematics.

The activities in this section are designed to be used by children without much adult help. It would be helpful, however, if children read the instructions with an adult present who can make sure they understand what is to be done. It is hoped that the games will be played many times and that the teacher will adapt the ideas to suit different groups of children and use them in other contexts. The puzzles on pages 47 to 59 are suitable for individual or class work. They are intended to be worked on for short periods of time and to be returned to, if necessary, for further work. Some of the puzzles are quite challenging and solving them should develop children's confidence and persistence.

Mathematical games provide teachers with ideal opportunities for assessment; for observing children and for listening to them in natural and relaxed contexts. Points to look for:

- Are children using mental recall where they can?
- Are they using the most effective strategies available to them?
- Are they developing their mental fluency and 'feel' for number?

Finally, it is good to remember that in order to produce the best mathematicians, we need to attend to their personal qualities. Children need to enjoy mathematics and feel willing to 'have a go'. This section should support that mission.

Triangles

Write numbers in the circles so that each side has a
total of 5. One has been done for you.

1.
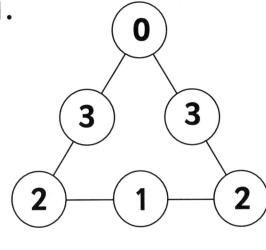

2.
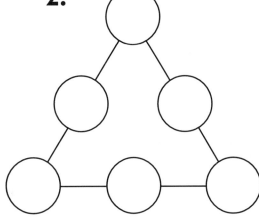

3.
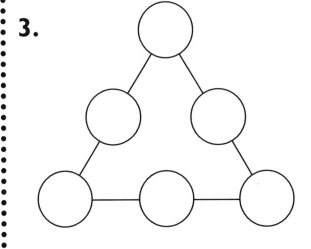

4.
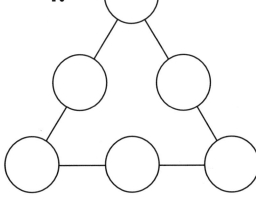

5.
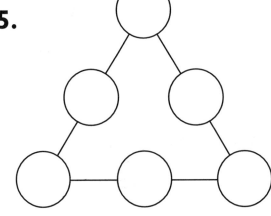

6.
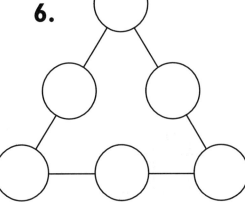

Name _____   **Date** _____

Missing numbers

Remind yourself of how numbers are marked on a number square.

Now, without looking at a number square, fill in the blank spaces.

1.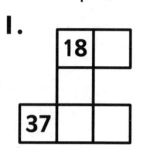

2.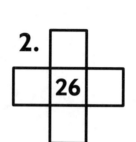

3.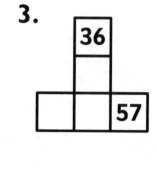

4.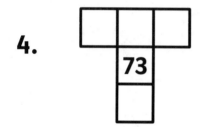

5.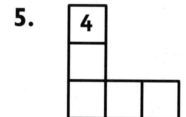

6.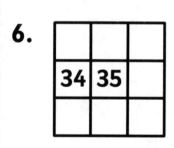

7.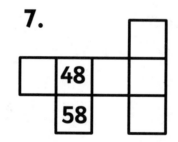

8.

9.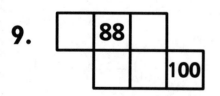

10.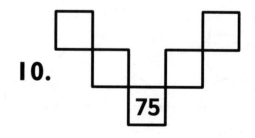

Name _____   **Date** _____

Missing coins

Some coins are missing from each of these purses.
Draw the missing coins on to the purses to make the
total amount.
You can use these coins:

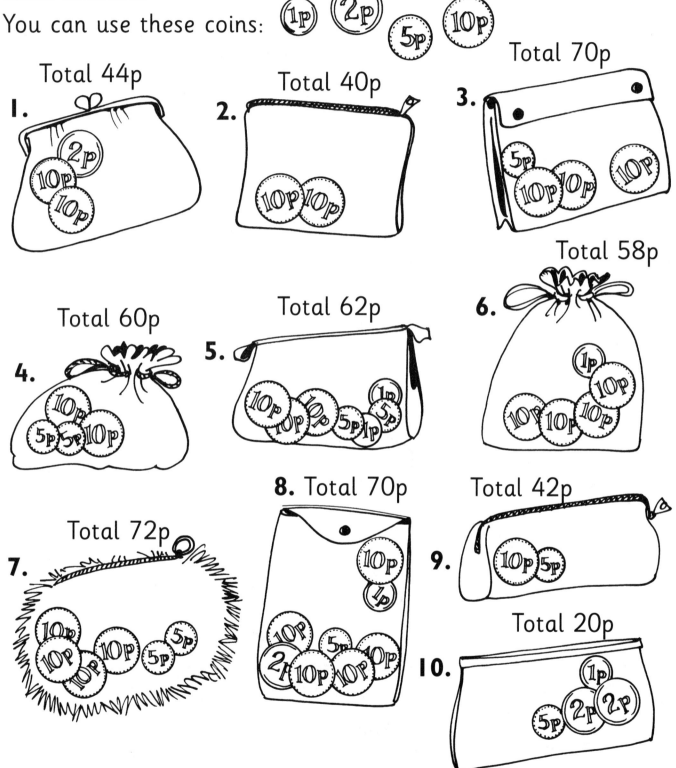

Total 44p

1.

Total 40p

2.

Total 70p

3.

Total 60p

4.

Total 62p

5.

Total 58p

6.

Total 72p

7.

8. Total 70p

Total 42p

9.

Total 20p

10.

Collins Mental Maths © HarperCollins*Publishers* Ltd 1998

Name _____   **Date** _____

Hops

Add a number and a **+** or **−** sign to each hop to land on the last number.

If you start on 25 and want to land on 50 in two hops you could do this:

Now try these.

1.

2.

3.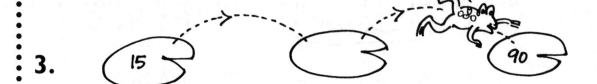

4.

5.

Name _____   **Date** _____

Hundred search

Search and find all the pairs of numbers which will give you a total of 100. You can go across, down or diagonally.

Two have been done for you.

49	87	52	11	42	32	66	25
13	61	49	48	68	33	85	63
39	44	52	45	42	74	15	33
59	31	22	55	26	64	26	77
29	64	69	65	78	53	87	23
71	46	76	22	57	47	39	41
39	54	73	38	57	43	61	38
48	71	72	27	62	39	58	62

Name _____ **Date** _____

Dice fortune A game for 2-3 players

You need: a die marked 1-6

- Each player should choose one of these numbers as their target number: 20, 30, 50.
- Take it in turns to throw the die. You can have up to 4 throws each time, but you may decide to have only one throw.
- Write down your score each time.
- If you throw a 1 you lose 10 points.
- The first player to reach their target number or over, wins.

Name _____ **Date** _____

Cross it out A game for 2 players

You need: two dice, one marked 2, 3, 3, 4, 4, 5 and the other one marked -1, -2, +3, +4, +5, +6; one copy each of these numbers:

0	1	2	3	4	5
6	7	8	9	10	11

- Take turns to throw the dice.
- Work out the sum of the two numbers and cross out the answer on your sheet. The first to cross out all the numbers wins.

Double power game A game for 2-3 players

You need: two dice, one marked 1-6 and the other marked 10, 10, 10, 10, 20, 20

- Each player takes it in turns to roll the two dice.
- After each dice throw, double both the numbers.
- Add up the numbers and write the total down as your score.
- The first person who reaches 100 or over, wins a round.
- Play four rounds.

Name _____ **Date** _____

Along the track A game for 2-3 players

You need: a die marked 1, 1, 2, 2, 3, 3, a counter in the colour of your choice, a sheet of paper and pen to write down the scores

- Each player starts with 100p.
- Take turns to throw the die and use the score to move around the track.
- Follow the instructions in the space where you land. The other players can help you to work out the sums if you get stuck.
- Keep a running total on the sheet of paper.
- The game comes to an end when all players have reached FINISH. You must get an exact number to land on FINISH. The winner is the player who has the most money left.

Name _____ **Date** _____

Darts challenge

You need: three counters to use as darts to throw at this dartboard

Work out the following.

- Show three different ways you can get a score of 10.

1 ....

2 ....

3 ....

- Show how you can get a score of 20.

....

- What is the highest score you can make with three darts?

....

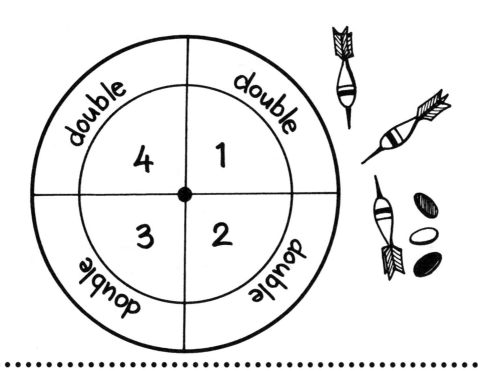

Name .... **Date** ....

Win a line A game for 2 players

You need: two dice marked 1-5, a set of counters in two different colours for each player

- Take it in turns to throw the two dice.
- Multiply the two numbers on the dice. Check the answer with your partner and cover the number with a counter.
- Take turns to cover the numbers on the grid to make winning lines of three across, down or diagonally.
- If a square has been covered, you cannot use the square again. If you get two winning lines, remove the counters and start again.
- Keep a score of your winning lines. The player who gets the most number of winning lines, wins.

1	16	4	10	3	20
3	10	2	16	8	6
5	8	5	6	25	12
4	9	15	12	5	20
12	6	4	25	9	1
10	8	2	15	16	8

Name _____ **Date** _____

Collins Mental Maths © HarperCollins Publishers Ltd 1998

Number star

These five numbers have been filled in on this number star:

(5) (6) (8) (15) (17)

- Cut out the number circles.
- Put the numbers on the star so that all four numbers in a straight line add up to 40.

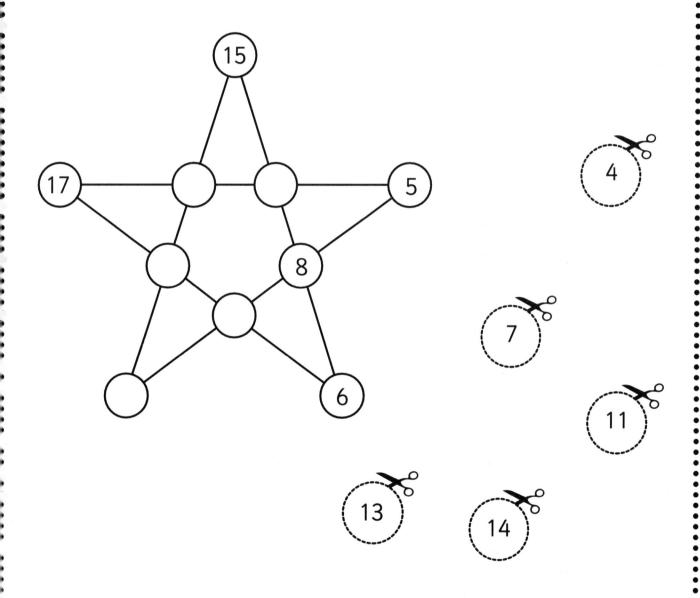

Name _____   **Date** _____

Two discs

You can see the numbers on one side of these two discs.

- Work out the numbers on the other two sides of the discs. Here is your clue. When you throw the two discs together, these are the only totals you will get:

The numbers are _____ and _____.

Missing numbers

The ☐ shape stands for **adding** a number.

The △ shape stands for **taking away** a number.

Fill in the signs and numbers for these.
One has been done for you.

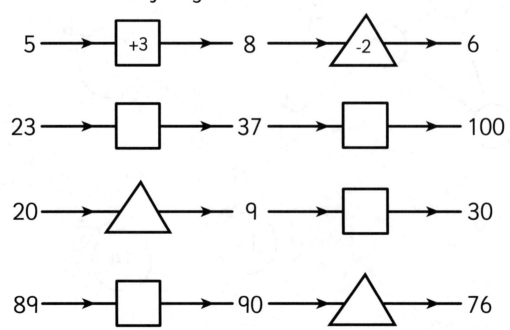

Name _____ **Date** _____

Magic

Write these numbers in each circle so that three numbers in a row each add up to 12.

1 2 3 4 5 6 7

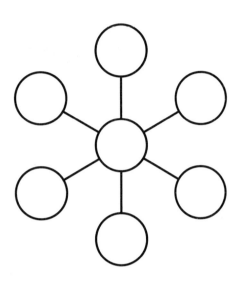

Fifteen

Place these numbers in the circles so that each one makes a total of 15.

1 2 3 4 5 6 7 8 9

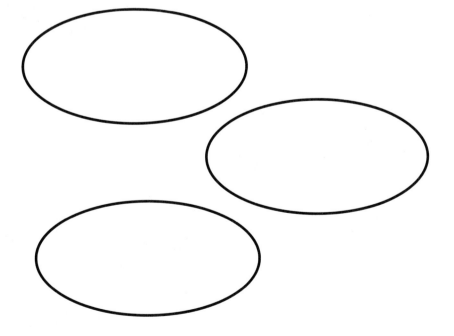

Name _____ **Date** _____

Teacher's Guide – Answers

SECTION 2

p11
1 4, 8, 8, 10, 5, 9, 9, 10, 7
2 3F, 4B, 2B, 4B, 4F

p13
1 Allow any combinations totalling to 10: 10 + 0; 9 + 1; 8 + 2; 7 + 3;
6 + 4; 5 + 5 and reverses.
2 Allow all correct calculations.

p15
1 Boat 5; Teddy Bear 4; Ball 6; Toy car 7; Cat 2; Dolls' clothes 1;
Dice 8; Horse 3
2 The sentence should read: You are a star.

p17
Allow all correct calculations which give a total of 10p.

p19
Allow all correct calculations, as there are many posssibilties for
this open-ended task.

p21
1 Accept any number which can be obtained by doubling a number.
2 Rings round: 8, 18, 22, 98, 68, 20, 40, 78, 36, 84, 82.

p23
1 In the addition square 2, 4, 6, 8, 10, 12, 14, 16, 18, 20 will have rings
round them.
2   5, 7, 11, 9
     13, 15, 19, 17
     7, 13, 9, 13
     9, 11, 7, 17
     21, 17, 11, 21

p25
1 Lots of possible ways of getting 20 with both 4 and 5 dice; accept
all correct calculations.

p27
1 20, 40, 61, 59, 53, 85
2 4 bunches and 2 singles, 3 bunches and 5 singles , 7 bunches and 2
singles.
3 35, 43, 68

p29
Accept all correct calculations for this open-ended task.

p31
Check the snakes for adding '1' on to odd numbers and 'halving
even' numbers patterns. For extension possibilities, it is worth
knowing that the longest snakes will have a power of two plus one
on their heads. The longest snakes, therefore, will have 4 + 1 = 5, 8 +
1 = 9, 16 + 1 = 17, 32 + 1 = 33, 64 + 1 = 65 and so on, on their heads.

p33
Orange = 60   Carrot = 75
Apple is worth more: Apple = 50 Banana = 33
Ant is worth more: Ant = 35 Bat = 23
Elephant is worth the most: Elephant = 81 Horse = 65 Koala = 40
Zebra = 52 Giraffe = 52
Hippopotamus is worth more = 169 Triceratops = 123
Sting is worth more = 69 Wasp = 59

p35
1 40, 50, 37, 37, 49, 58, 58, 69, 88, 92, 74
2 30, 40, 41, 49, 49, 61, 49, 35, 62

p37
1 26
2 40
3 Accept 9 or 27
4 41

60

p39
1 8 13 16 12 8
10 40 20 10
2 Open-ended possibilites, accept all correct calculations.

p41
(1-3) Accept any solution showing an understanding of the concepts of
half, quarter and a third.

Ticks for half of 12; half of 24; half of 36; quarter of 88; half of 50.

SECTION 3

Puzzle 1
Several options especially when using a zero which is allowed.

Puzzle 2

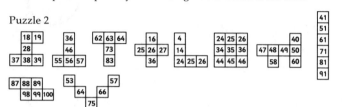

Puzzle 3
Ensure that the coins add up to the total on each purse.

Puzzle 4
Accept all correct ways for this very open-ended task.

Puzzle 5

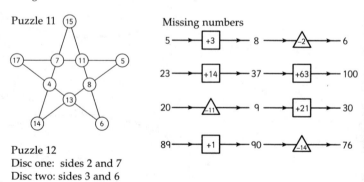

Puzzle 9
1 Accept any combination of a total of 10.
2 Highest = 24

Puzzle 11

Missing numbers

$5 \longrightarrow \boxed{+3} \longrightarrow 8 \longrightarrow \triangle_{-2} \longrightarrow 6$

$23 \longrightarrow \boxed{+14} \longrightarrow 37 \longrightarrow \boxed{+63} \longrightarrow 100$

$20 \longrightarrow \triangle_{-11} \longrightarrow 9 \longrightarrow \boxed{+21} \longrightarrow 30$

$89 \longrightarrow \boxed{+1} \longrightarrow 90 \longrightarrow \triangle_{-14} \longrightarrow 76$

Puzzle 12
Disc one: sides 2 and 7
Disc two: sides 3 and 6

Puzzle 13

One solution is:

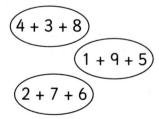

Answers

PUPIL BOOK 1

p2
1 5
2 8
3 3
4 1
5 6
6 8, 9
7 4, 5
8 7
9 9
10 6
11 4
12 2

p3
1 3
2 10
3 6
4 0
5 5
6 2, 1
7 7, 6
8 2
9 6
10 1
11 5
12 5

p4
1 3
2 4
3 5
4 5
5 2
6 2
7 3
8 4
9 0
10 2
11 1
12 3

triangles
top row 2, 2, 1
bottom row 1, 1

p5
1 7
2 7
3 7
4 5
5 6
6 9
7 5
8 10
9 8
10 4
11 10
12 8

purses
a 5p or 5 x 1p or 2 x 2p + 1p or 3 x 1p + 2p
b 2p + 1p or 2 x 1p + 2p
c as b
d 2p or 2 x 1p

p6
1 5
2 5
3 9
4 7, 8
5 8
6 7
7 6
8 7
9 6
10 6
11 7
12 10
purses
a 8p
b 7p
c 4p

p7
1 13
2 10
3 19
4 14
5 13
6 11
7 15
8 10
9 19
10 9
11 12
12 15

p8
1 30
2 60
3 80
4 30
5 80
6 20
7 50
8 80
9 90
10 30
11 10
12 40

p9
1 6
2 14
3 9
4 17
5 7
6 12

7 15
8 16
9 10
10 20
11 true
12 false

p10
1 1
2 4
3 6
4 8
5 3
6 2
7 6
8 any addition bond to 10 eg 6 + 4
9 2
10 any subtraction giving 5 as the answer eg 7 - 2
11 7
12 any subtraction giving 7 as the answer eg 8 - 1
Squares
a 2
b 3
c 1

p11
1 4
2 6
3 4
4 5 + 5
5 2
6 8
7 1 + 1
8 3
9 0
10 10
11 1
12 6

dominoes top row
double 3 is 6
double 5 is 10
double 2 is 4
bottom row
double 4 is 8
double 1 is 2

p12
1 2
2 9
3 8
4 9
5 4
6 6
7 20
8 2
9 9
10 13
11 3
12 9
clowns
a 7
b 18, 20
c 11, 10

p13

1 14
2 6
3 3
4 2
5 16p
6 10
7 10
8 5
9 19
10 12
11 8
12 4
Shopping
1 9p
2 8p
3 7p
4 5p

p14
1 25
2 28p
3 16
4 11
5 4
6 9
7 3
8 8
9 24
10 13
11 4
12 20

Shopping
1 14p
2 11p
3 10p
4 12p
5 4p

p15
1 19
2 4
3 18
4 13
5 17
6 12
7 16
8 3
9 3
10 19
11 18
12 13
How old
1 17
2 12
3 18
4 11

p16
1 19
2 50
3 16p
4 15
5 60
6 9
7 3
8 6
9 10
10 8p

11 18
12 20
Totals
1 7 + 3 or 3 + 7 or 5 + 5
2 7 + 5 or 5 + 7
3 5 + 3 or 3 + 5
4 10 + 7 or 7 + 10

p17
1 12
2 12
3 3
4 5
5 14p
6 6
7 13
8 15
9 any addition with a
total of 17 eg 9 + 8
10 8p
11 7
12 any addition with a
total of 15 eg 8 + 7

Complete the missing
numbers
1 3, 3
2 3, 12
3 8, 10
4 4, 4, 14

p18
1 12
2 7
3 10
4 8
5 10
6 8
7 18
8 10
9 14
10 5
11 16
12 6
Playing cards
double 3 is 6
double 4 is 8
double 2 is 4

p19
1 13
2 17
3 11
4 15
5 9
6 19

Adding 9
1 12
2 14
3 17
4 15
5 13
6 18

p20
1 16
2 15
3 7

4 11p
5 13
6 6
7 7
8 7
9 18
10 any combination to
make 17 eg 9 + 8
11 14p
12 any combination to
make 13 = 7 + 6

Making 20
1 4
2 7
3 13
4 9

p21
1 7p
2 18
3 11
4 2
5 8p
6 9
7 1
8 8
9 0
10 3
11 9
12 1

p22
any number within the
following range is correct
1 3-6
2 6-9
3 8-11
4 7-10
5 4
6 11-14
7 14-18
8 19
9 21-29
10 20-23
True or false?
1 true
2 false
3 true
4 false
5 true

p23
1 6, 7, 8, 9
2 2, 4, 8, 9
3 5, 10, 16, 18
4 7, 5, 3, 2, 0
5 21, 20, 17, 15
6 12, 10, 9, 3
any one number within
the range is acceptable for
numbers 7-9
7 3-4
8 11-14
9 18
all numbers in the range
must be given for 10-12
10 24, 25, 26, 27
11 10, 11

12 14, 15, 16, 17, 18, 19

p24
1 a
2 e
3 j
4 h
5 c
6 l
7 d
8 b
9 k
10 f
11 i
12 g

p25
1 6, 7 or 8
2 19
3 false
4 true
5 false
6 16, 14, 12, 9, 8
7 24, 22, 19, 17
8 any of: 10, 11, 12, 13 or
14
9 false
10 15p
11 4, 10, 14, 24
12 10p, 20p, 23p, 30p

p26
1 9
2 10
3 12p
4 11
5 2
6 4
7 1p
8 2
9 any pair of numbers
totalling 11
10 any 3 numbers that
add up to 10
11 any pair of numbers
that add up to 11
12 2
Triangles
1 any 3 numbers that
make 17 eg 5 + 6 + 6
2 any 3 numbers that
make 11 eg 6 + 3 + 2
3 any 3 numbers that
make 19 eg 10 + 5 + 4

p27
1 8 = 5 + 3 or 3 + 5
2 5 = 2 + 3 or 3 + 2
3 7 = 5 + 2 or 2 + 5
4 10 = 5 + 3 + 2

5, 6, 7 and 8 all require
addition sums using 1, 2,
5 and 6
9-12 all involve addition
sums using 4, 6, 7 and 9

p28
1 16

2 20
3 27
4 42
5 20
6 49
7 13
8 12
9 60
10 22
11 3
12 9

True or false?
1 false
2 false
3 false
4 false
5 false

p29
1 15
2 10
3 20
4 40
5 50
6 19
7 28
8 12
9 40
10 3
11 17
12 10
Number hops
1 16
2 9
3 30, 40

p30
1 15
2 6
3 30
4 3
5 0
6 7 + 4 or 4 + 7
7 4 + 5 or 5 + 4
8 7 + 4 + 5
9 40
10 28
11 5p
12 any 3 numbers that
add up to 16 eg 10 + 5 + 1

p31
1 17p
2 17p
3 35p
4 16p
5 50p
6 26p
7 10p
8 17p

Answers

PUPIL BOOK 2

p2 1 more or less
1 18
2 35
3 58
4 29
5 90
6 8
7 11
8 40
9 56
10 79

Counting in 10s
1 40
2 80
3 100
4 10
5 30
6 50
7 50
8 80
9 10
10 40

p3 Counting in 2s
1 8
2 19
3 28
4 18
5 30
6 19
7 30, 32
8 9, 7
9 32, 30
10 29, 31

Odd and even
1 12, 18, 20
2 20
3 16, 26
4 7, 3
5 33, 37
6 11, 13, 15, 17, 19
7 21
8 10
9 30
10 9

p4 Ten more
1 38
2 74
3 48
4 99
5 101
6 0
7 22
8 47
9 66
10 95

Large and small
1 23p
2 54
3 13kg
4 13cm
5 2
6 20
7 23
8 95
9 86
10 71

p5 In between
1 28, 29, or 30
2 29, 20, 21, 22, 23 or 24
3 55, 56, 57, 58 or 59
4 76, 77, 78, 79 or 80
5 90 or 91
6 9

7 25
8 47
9 95p
10 55cm

Ordering numbers
1 83, 57, 47, 29, 16
2 50p, 45p, 35p, 20p
3 91 cm, 21 cm, 19 cm, 9 cm
4 11p, 13p, 23p, 31p
5 49, 57, 68, 78, 96
6 25 kg, 35 kg, 67 kg, 68 kg
7 24, 25, 26 or 27 and 29, 30, 31, 32, 33 or 34
8 55, 56, 57, 58 or 59 and 61, 62, 63, 64, 65, 66, 67 or 68
9 79, 80 or 81 and 83, 84 or 85
10 91 and 93, 94, 95 96, 97, 98 or 99

p6
1 66
2 89
3 70
4 90
5 100
6 65p
7 1cm
8 false
9 22, 24, 26 and 28
10 87, 89, 91 and 93
11 2, 0
12 99, 101
13 51, 49
14 11, 12, 15, 17, 19
15 2, 12. 20, 21, 22
16 false
17 true
18 true
19 true
20 false

p7 Addition to 10
1 7
2 8
3 2
4 any pair of numbers that add up to 9
5 7p
6 10
7 8
8 any pair of numbers that add up to 7
9 8
10 4

Subtraction to 10
1 4p
2 8
3 6
4 2
5 2 cm
6 4
7 any subtraction with an answer of 5 eg 9 - 4
8 9
9 8
10 9

p8 Adding 3 numbers
1 9
2 15
3 16p
4 5
5 23
6 any addition sum with 3 numbers including 7 and 11
7 4

8 any addition sum with 3 numbers totalling 18
9 17
10 any 3 numbers that add up to 20

Doubles and halves
1 16
2 20
3 12
4 5
5 14
6 4
7 18
8 24
9 15
10 26

p9 Making 20
1 14
2 2
3 5
4 13
5 10
6 8
7 20
8 16
9 19
10 3

Making 100
1 30
2 50
3 90
4 80
5 60
6 100
7 50
8 70
9 40
10 20

p10 Doubles and halves 2
1 40
2 60
3 25
4 30
5 100
6 35
7 90
8 80
9 10
10 50

Near doubles
1 17
2 41
3 59
4 15
5 11
6 31
7 13
8 21
9 81
10 99

p11 Counting on or back
1 14
2 24
3 29
4 24
5 32
6 36
7 18
8 100
9 30
10 30

Find the difference
1 5
2 3
3 3
4 4p
5 4
6 6p
7 6
8 6
9 4
10 5

p12 Adding 9 or 19
1 32
2 26
3 44

4 57
5 81
6 34
7 47
8 51
9 60
10 73

Subtracting 9 or 19
1 7
2 22
3 36
4 58
5 71
6 15
7 32
8 48
9 54
10 61

p13 Adding 11 or 21
1 29
2 48
3 69
4 90
5 54
6 53
7 67
8 89
9 100
10 80

Subtracting 11 or 21
1 24
2 38
3 39
4 69
5 87
6 18
7 47
8 29
9 69
10 66

p14
1 50
2 14
3 70
4 72
5 21
6 9
7 48
8 17p
9 25
10 79
11 13
12 any pair of numbers that add up to 19
13 30
14 4p
15 69
16 7
17 60
18 75
19 39
20 90

p15 Patterns
1 9, 19, 29, 59
2 2, 12, 22, 72
3 8, 80, 620
4 5, 50, 500

Number sequences
1 3 + 5 = 8, 5 + 3 = 8, 8 - 3 = 5, 8 - 5 = 3
2 8 + 2 = 10, 2 + 8 = 10, 10 - 8 = 2, 10 - 2 = 8

p16 Adding and subtracting single digits
1 29
2 7
3 42
4 53
5 5
6 84
7 67
8 98
9 71

Adding to multiples of 10 and 100
1 43

2 507
3 7
4 2
5 80
6 500
7 4
8 59
9 206
10 900

p17 Subtracting from multiples of 10
1 38
2 73
3 6
4 8
5 51
6 26
7 70
8 50
9 67
10 90

Adding 2 digits to a multiple of 10
1 44
2 67
3 93
4 60
5 20
6 31
7 86
8 72
9 15
10 37

p18 Adding or subtracting 'teens' numbers
1 38
2 13
3 71
4 13
5 45p
6 15
7 51
8 61
9 16
10 33p

Adding or subtracting 10
1 37
2 46
3 75
4 68
5 73
6 59
7 49
8 84
9 82
10 99

p19 More tens
1 50
2 any pair of numbers adding up to 80
3 70
4 20
5 a pair of numbers with a difference of 40
6 30
7 90
8 50
9 40
10 any pair of numbers that add up to 60

Adding or subtracting multiples of 10
1 74
2 26
3 86
4 30
5 29
6 20
7 91
8 40
9 30
10 83

p20 Adding or subtracting hundreds
1 700
2 300

3 600
4 800
5 200
6 any pair of numbers that add up to 500
7 any pair of numbers with a difference of 100
8 200
9 800
10 700
shapes top row 100 rectangle, 300 triangle
bottom row 200 rectangle 200 triangle

p21 Crossing 10
1 13
2 13
3 15
4 9
5 9
6 8
7 22
8 5
9 17
10 any pair of numbers with a total of 13

Crossing 20
1 24
2 18
3 18
4 22
5 8
6 23
7 7
8 18
9 22
10 19

p22 What's the difference
1 8
2 3
3 7
4 8
5 4
6 6
7 59
8 70
9 34
10 51

Ordinal numbers
1 c
2 t
3 e
4 p
5 b
6 v
7 d
8 j
9 l
10 x

p23
1 14
2 47
3 6
4 300
5 90
6 d
7 47
8 any pair of numbers with a total of 900
9 57
10 64
11 3
12 802
13 7
14 600
15 October
16 60
17 any pair of numbers with a difference of 100
18 9, 19, 29
19 5, 15, 35
20 9, 90, 900

p24 Multiplying by 1 and 10
1 50
2 4
3 10

4 7
5 8
6 10
7 60
8 10
9 3
10 any pair of numbers with a product of 40

Dividing by 1 and 10
1 7
2 3
3 10
4 1
5 2
6 7
7 10
8 1
9 children write their own sentence dividing by 10
10 6

p25 Multiplying by 2
1 12
2 2
3 6
4 1
5 5
6 20
7 7
8 18
9 0
10 2

Dividing by 2
1 10
2 5
3 7
4 8
5 4
6 9
7 8
8 24
9 2
10 6

p26 Multiplying by 5
1 15
2 7
3 50
4 2
5 5 x 5
6 9
7 5
8 4
9 8
10 30

Multiplying by 3
1 12
2 6
3 1
4 9
5 3 x 3
6 21
7 2
8 15
9 24
10 10

p27 Multiplying by 4
1 0
2 5
3 24
4 4 x 4
5 36
6 4
7 7
8 3
9 10
10 32

More multiplying by 2
1 26
2 42
3 66
4 12
5 31
6 44
7 82
8 34
9 42
10 28

p28 Multiplying and adding
1 3
2 27
3 2
4 14
5 3
6 29
7 43
8 6
9 12
10 45

Mixed multiplying
1 12
2 50
3 18
4 6
5 70
6 0
7 30
8 8
9 20
10 0

p29 Different divisions
1 5
2 6
3 6
4 3
5 10
6 3
7 10
8 9
9 8
10 9

Fractions
1 10
2 6
3 8
4 9
5 4
6 7
7 10
8 3
9 2
10 5

p30 Money
1 5p, 2p, 1p
2 10p, 2p, 1p
3 20p, 5p, 1p
4 10p, 5p, 2p
5 10p
6 24p
7 80
8 55
9 5
10 12
11 25
12 60p
13 80p
14 100p or £1
15 £15
16 £20
17 26p
18 15p
19 8p
20 1p

p31
1 15
2 14
3 5
4 9
5 0
6 10
7 6
8 26
9 9
10 5
11 73p
12 13
13 5
14 30
15 2
16 £10
17 10
18 3
19 1